How to use cards

Choose the card that suits the picture you want to take and place in shot.

Take your photo then share the Halloween fun with your family.

There are blank cards for you to personalise with your own messages and spooky games to play.

Use a wipe-clean pen to write on the cards. To remove a card first lay the book open on a flat surface. Then carefully tear, or pull the card away from the centre of the book, starting from the top left corner.

TRICK OR TREAT

This Halloween I'm dressed as

MAKE a memory

HAPPY HALLOWEEN!

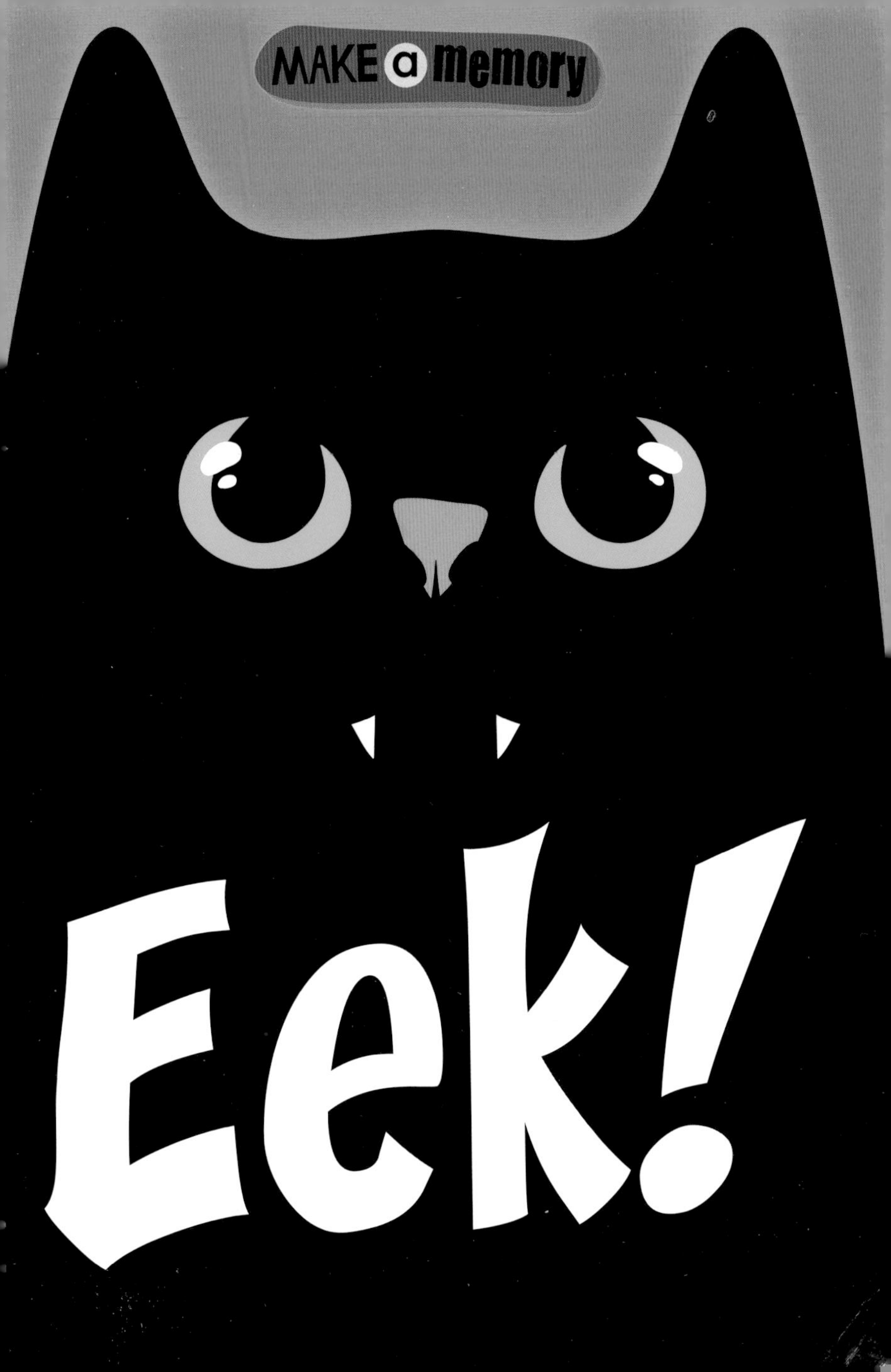
MAKE a memory
Eek!

MAKE a memory

MY PUMPKIN IS THE BEST!

MAKE a memory

Fang-tastic

SPOOKTACULAR!

SPOOKIEST GUEST

MAKE a memory

I ATE ALL MY TREATS!

BEWARE OF THE MUMMY

MAKE a memory

WATCH OUT FOR COBWEBS

I carved a

in my pumpkin

ARE YOU SCARED YET?

Spooky but cute!

MY FAVOURITE TRICK IS

MAKE a memory

FRIGHT-FULLY FUN PARTY

MAKE a memory

ENTER

AT YOUR OWN RISK

MAKE a memory

EAT, DRINK AND BE SCARY!

ONLY THE SPOOKY WILL SURVIVE

MAKE a memory

MAKE a memory

PUMPKIN PATCH

MONSTROUS MUNCHIES

SQUISHIES

MAKE a memory

KEEP YOUR WIG ON!

MASK?
WHAT
MASK?

YOU'RE IN MY SPIDER WEB

ME AND MY GHOUL-FRIENDS!

YOU'RE MY FAVOURITE SPOOK!

MAKE a memory

HAPPY

HAUNTING

BLACK CAT COMING THIS WAY

MAKE a memory

WELCOME GHOULS

CREEPY CUPCAKES

MAKE a memory

MONSTER-WORTHY

GHOULISH GHOULASH ANYONE?

BE
GHOSTLY

SPOOKY GAMES

Make some spooky memories
by playing these ghoulish games.

—— DONUT CHOMP ——

Place a sugar-coated donut on a paper
plate and put your hands behind your back.
The game is to try to eat the donut without
using your hands. You can make the game
even tougher by not licking your lips!

—— GHOST FREEZE ——

Similar to 'Musical Statues', put some spooky
Halloween music on then stop dancing
whenever the music pauses. Whoever is
moving when the music stops must leave the
game. The winner is the last dancer dancing.

—— SPIDER WEB ——

Draw a spider's web on a large piece of
paper. Then secure a piece of rolled-up
sticky tape underneath a small plastic spider.
Blindfold the players, and now you can play
'Stick the Spider on the Web'.

MORE HALLOWEEN GAMES

Here are some more ghoulish games to inspire some spooky memories!

—— POP GOES THE PUMPKIN ——

Before they are blown up, fill orange balloons with small, individually wrapped sweets or chocolate coins. The game is to stomp on and pop as many inflated balloons, or 'pumpkins' as you can.

Always check before playing in case anyone has an allergy to balloon rubber/latex.

—— ZOMBIE STATUES ——

Similar to 'Ghost Freeze', but when the music is paused everyone pretends to be zombies. Anyone who is dancing when the music is paused is 'out' and must leave the game. The winner is the last zombie left!

—— BOWLING FOR GHOSTS ——

Draw on, or stick googly eyes on to 10 toilet rolls. Then stack the rolls on top of each other in a pyramid. Using a small ball, now see how many ghosts you can knock over as you bowl the ball at the stack of ghosts.

PHOTO SCAVENGER HUNT

Can you get a photo of everything
on this list during Halloween?

- ☐ A GHOST
- ☐ A WITCH
- ☐ A CARVED PUMPKIN
- ☐ A MONSTER
- ☐ START OF THE PARTY
- ☐ PARTY FOOD
- ☐ SOMETHING THAT GLOWS IN THE DARK
- ☐ A SKELETON
- ☐ A BALLOON
- ☐ A VAMPIRE

- ☐ TRICK OR TREAT
- ☐ YOUR REFLECTION
- ☐ A SPOOKY SIGN
- ☐ SOMETHING TASTY
- ☐ A SPIDER
- ☐ TRICK OR TREAT SWEETS
- ☐ SOMEONE DANCING
- ☐ A FUN COSTUME
- ☐ A MASK
- ☐ END OF THE PARTY

HALLOWEEN CHALLENGES

SPLIT INTO TWO TEAMS AND COMPETE IN THESE GHOULISH GAMES AT YOUR HALLOWEEN PARTY.

Team 1: _____   Team 2: _____

Challenge 1 : Wrap the Mummy

YOU'LL NEED A TOILET ROLL PER TEAM. ONE PLAYER FROM EACH TEAM IS THE MUMMY, THE OTHER PLAYERS MUST RACE TO WRAP THEIR MUMMY AS FAST AS THEY CAN. WINNER: _____

Challenge 2 : Mummy Race

MARK OUT A RACETRACK AROUND YOUR GARDEN. THEN THE MUMMIES MUST RACE AROUND THE TRACK WITHOUT RIPPING THEIR PAPER WRAPPINGS. FIRST TO FINISH WINS! WINNER: _____

Challenge 3 : Apple Bobbing

FILL A WASHING-UP BOWL WITH WATER AND LOTS OF APPLES. EACH TEAM MUST TAKE IT IN TURNS TO BOB FOR APPLES. THE TEAM WITH THE MOST APPLES WINS! WINNER: _____

MAKE a memory